Positive Mindset Journal for Teachers

A year of happy thoughts, inspirational quotes, and reflections **for a positive teaching experience**

D1468778

Grace Stevens

Paperback Edition

ISBN: 978 0 9980 19-1-2

Manufactured in the United States of America

Red Lotus Books,
Mountain House CA

Red Lotus Books

This journal belongs to:

_____

School Year: _____

" *Learning is the only thing the mind never exhausts, never fears and never regrets. It is the only thing that will never fail us.*"

Leonardo da Vinci

How To Use This Book

The goal of this journal is to help you connect to the parts of your teaching week that bring you joy. While there is plenty of research to support the idea that a positive classroom environment will increase student engagement and achievement, this journal isn't for your students' benefits; it's for yours. You deserve to enjoy your teaching day!

Teaching is a "noble profession." We choose it because we know it is important, not necessarily because we believe it will be easy. But teaching can and should be fun and rewarding. Many years of experience in the classroom have taught me that everyone's day goes smoother when the teacher is happy. I have also learned that there are specific things that I can do to train my mind to focus on the "good stuff", seek out opportunities to make a student's, a parent's or a co-worker's day and remind myself of how awesome a privilege it really is to spend my day with children.

This journal is designed to help you take a few moments to reflect on your intentions before the work week gets rolling and it's momentum gets you into "survival mode." How will you take care of **your** needs? Who can you celebrate? Who can you thank?

Taking a few minutes to write down the best parts of your day before you go home will put you in a better mental space and train your mind to be a "joy detective," focusing on the good stuff. Training your brain to seek out things you are grateful for and inspired by is simply a habit. If you work on flexing your "happy muscle" daily, you will find it easier to connect to joy in your day and share that joy with others. This humble journal can help you do that.

Leave this journal on your desk and commit to writing in it every day for three weeks. Three weeks is all it takes to form a new habit. You will find that taking a few moments to smile and reflect every day will help turn you into a "joy detective," eager to find things in your teaching day that bring you gratitude, appreciation and smiley faces.

If you keep up this happy journaling habit, at the end of the school year, you will have a treasured keepsake of a window in time that you shared with a unique group of students. No two classes are the same, and each teaching year is different.

My hope is that this journal can help you connect in the moment, and in years to come, to the best of times, the best of your students and the best of yourself. Failing that, at least you might have a few cool doodles.

Wishing you a wonderful year, and many joy-filled moments!

Grace

P.S. This journal is a companion piece to a book I wrote called _Positive Mindset Habits for Teachers - 10 Steps to Reduce Stress, Increase Student Engagement and Reignite Your Passion for Teaching._ You can use this journal as a stand alone piece, but if you are serious about transforming your teaching, I think you will really enjoy the book too. You can find it on Amazon and at happy-classrooms.com

Beginning of Year Intentions

What are some ways I can ensure my students and I have the most positive classroom experience this year?

_____

_____

_____

_____

_____

_____

Some things I already do that I love and should KEEP

_____

_____

_____

Some things that would be helpful to CHANGE

_____

_____

_____

Some things that would be helpful to START

_____

_____

_____

_____

_____

What are some things I love doing *outside* of school that I can commit to engaging in to ensure I stay energized, excited about teaching, and happy in general?

_____

_____

_____

_____

_____

_____

_____

_____

Who is going to be my "life line" in my professional life this year? Who is the person I can rely on for input, advice, a shoulder to lean on, my "safe place," or just someone to laugh and celebrate with?

_____

_____

Who will be the "life lines" in my personal life?

_____

_____

_____

Which colleague or colleagues can I develop a closer

relationship with this year? (Can I be someone's life line?)

_____

_____

_____

_____

_____

_____

Notes from Professional Development

What "take aways" do I have from the beginning of the year Professional Development? Which ideas can I immediately implement before they get forgotten? Which ones in particular might contribute to a more joyful classroom experience?

_____

_____

_____

_____

_____

_____

_____

_____

_____

_____

_____

_____

Notes from Professional Development

_____

_____

_____

_____

_____

_____

_____

_____

_____

_____

_____

OK, you're all set, let's rock this year!

> *"Like the sun, a teacher enlightens a mind with his love, warmth, and light."*
>
> Debasish Mridha

Date _____

My intention for this week:

_____

_____

_____

Who I can champion this week:

_____

Three Ways I Can Take Care of Myself This Week:

❧ 1. _____

❧ 2. _____

❧ 3. _____

The best three parts of today:

Monday:

1. _____

2. _____

3. _____

Tuesday:

1. _____

2. _____

3. _____

Wednesday:

1. _____

2. _____

3. _____

The best three parts of today:

Thursday:

1. _____

2. _____

3. _____

Friday:

1. _____

2. _____

3. _____

Something I am especially grateful for this week:

_____

_____

_____

Quote of the Week: (funniest thing a student said, a compliment you were given, or something inspirational you read)

Three people I can **thank** or **celebrate** this week - in person, in writing, or by making a "day maker" phone call, text or e-mail.

❥ _____ ☐

❥ _____ ☐

❥ _____ ☐

Check as you complete ☑

Random Doodle Box

> *"Teaching is not about how we see things, it is about how children see things."*
>
> Kavita Bhupta Ghosh

Date _____

My intention for this week:

_____

_____

_____

Who I can champion this week:

_____

Three Ways I Can Take Care of Myself This Week:

❥ 1. _____

❥ 2. _____

❥ 3. _____

The best three parts of today:

Monday:

1. _____

2. _____

3. _____

Tuesday:

1. _____

2. _____

3. _____

Wednesday:

1. _____

2. _____

3. _____

The best three parts of today:

Thursday:

1. _____

2. _____

3. _____

Friday:

1. _____

2. _____

3. _____

Something I am especially grateful for this week:

_____

_____

_____

Quote of the Week: (funniest thing a student said, a compliment you were given, something inspirational you read)

Three people I can **thank** or **celebrate** this week - in person, in writing, or by making a "day maker" phone call, text or e-mail.

❥ _____ ☐

❥ _____ ☐

❥ _____ ☐

Check as you complete ☑

Random Coloring Box

"Positive expectations are the mark of the superior personality."

Brian Tracy

Date _____

My intention for this week:

_____

_____

_____

Who I can champion this week:

_____

Three Ways I Can Take Care of Myself This Week:

❧ 1._____

❧ 2._____

❧ 3._____

The best three parts of today:

Monday:

1. _____

2. _____

3. _____

Tuesday:

1. _____

2. _____

3. _____

Wednesday:

1. _____

2. _____

3. _____

The best three parts of today:

Thursday:

1. _____

2. _____

3. _____

Friday:

1. _____

2. _____

3. _____

Something I am especially grateful for this week:

_____

_____

_____

Quote of the Week: (funniest thing a student said, a compliment you were given, something inspirational you read)

Three people I can **thank** or **celebrate** this week - in person, in writing, or by making a "day maker" phone call, text or e-mail.

❧ _____ ☐

❧ _____ ☐

❧ _____ ☐

Check as you complete ☑

Random Doodle Box

> *"I never teach my pupils, I only attempt to provide the conditions in which they can learn."*
>
> Albert Einstein

Date _____

My intention for this week:

_____

_____

_____

Who I can champion this week:

_____

Three Ways I Can Take Care of Myself This Week:

❥ 1. _____

❥ 2. _____

❥ 3. _____

The best three parts of today:

Monday:

    1. _____

    2. _____

    3. _____

Tuesday:

    1. _____

    2. _____

    3. _____

Wednesday:

    1. _____

    2. _____

    3. _____

The best three parts of today:

Thursday:

1. _____

2. _____

3. _____

Friday:

1. _____

2. _____

3. _____

Something I am especially grateful for this week:

_____

_____

_____

Quote of the Week: (funniest thing a student said, a compliment you were given, something inspirational you read)

Three people I can **thank** or **celebrate** this week - in person, in writing, or by making a "day maker" phone call, text or e-mail.

➤ _____ ☐

➤ _____ ☐

➤ _____ ☐

Check as you complete ☑

Random
Doodle
Box

> *"Thousands of candles can be lighted from a single candle, and the life of the candle will not be shortened. Happiness never decreases by being shared. "*
>
> Buddha

Date _____

My intention for this week:

_____

_____

_____

Who I can champion this week:

_____

Three Ways I Can Take Care of Myself This Week:

❥ 1. _____

❥ 2. _____

❥ 3. _____

The best three parts of today:

Monday:

    1. _____

    2. _____

    3. _____

Tuesday:

    1. _____

    2. _____

    3. _____

Wednesday:

    1. _____

    2. _____

    3. _____

The best three parts of today:

Thursday:

1. _____

2. _____

3. _____

Friday:

1. _____

2. _____

3. _____

Something I am especially grateful for this week:

_____

_____

_____

Quote of the Week: (funniest thing a student said, a compliment you were given, something inspirational you read)

Three people I can **thank** or **celebrate** this week - in person, in writing, or by making a "day maker" phone call, text or e-mail.

❥ _____ ☐

❥ _____ ☐

❥ _____ ☐

Check as you complete ☑

Random Doodle Box

"It is easier to build strong children than to repair broken men. "

Frederick Douglas

Date _____

My intention for this week:

_____

_____

_____

Who I can champion this week:

_____

Three Ways I Can Take Care of Myself This Week:

❥ 1._____

❥ 2._____

❥ 3._____

The best three parts of today:

Monday:

   1. _____

   2. _____

   3. _____

Tuesday:

   1. _____

   2. _____

   3. _____

Wednesday:

   1. _____

   2. _____

   3. _____

The best three parts of today:

Thursday:

1. _____

2. _____

3. _____

Friday:

1. _____

2. _____

3. _____

Something I am especially grateful for this week:

_____

_____

_____

Quote of the Week: (funniest thing a student said, a compliment you were given, something inspirational you read)

Three people I can **thank** or **celebrate** this week - in person, in writing, or by making a "day maker" phone call, text or e-mail.

❥ _____ ☐

❥ _____ ☐

❥ _____ ☐

Check as you complete ☑

Random
Doodle
Box

> *"Someone is sitting in the shade today because someone planted a tree a long time ago. "*
>
> Warren Buffett

Date _____

My intention for this week:

_____

_____

_____

Who I can champion this week:

_____

Three Ways I Can Take Care of Myself This Week:

❥ 1._____

❥ 2._____

❥ 3._____

The best three parts of today:

Monday:

1. _____

2. _____

3. _____

Tuesday:

1. _____

2. _____

3. _____

Wednesday:

1. _____

2. _____

3. _____

The best three parts of today:

Thursday:

1. _____

2. _____

3. _____

Friday:

1. _____

2. _____

3. _____

Something I am especially grateful for this week:

_____

_____

_____

Quote of the Week: (funniest thing a student said, a compliment you were given, something inspirational you read)

Three people I can **thank** or **celebrate** this week - in person, in writing, or by making a "day maker" phone call, text or e-mail.

❥ _____ ☐

❥ _____ ☐

❥ _____ ☐

Check as you complete ☑

Random Doodle Box

> *"Change your thoughts and you change your world."*
>
> Norman Vincent Peale

Date _____

My intention for this week:

_____

_____

_____

Who I can champion this week:

_____

Three Ways I Can Take Care of Myself This Week:

❥ 1. _____

❥ 2. _____

❥ 3. _____

The best three parts of today:

Monday:

    1. _____

    2. _____

    3. _____

Tuesday:

    1. _____

    2. _____

    3. _____

Wednesday:

    1. _____

    2. _____

    3. _____

The best three parts of today:

Thursday:

    1. _____

    2. _____

    3. _____

Friday:

    1. _____

    2. _____

    3. _____

Something I am especially grateful for this week:

_____

_____

_____

Quote of the Week: (funniest thing a student said, a compliment you were given, something inspirational you read)

Three people I can **thank** or **celebrate** this week - in person, in writing, or by making a "day maker" phone call, text or e-mail.

➤ _____ ☐

➤ _____ ☐

➤ _____ ☐

Check as you complete

Random
Doodle
Box

> *"Let us remember: One book, one pen, one child, and one teacher can change the world. "*
>
> Malala Yousafzai

Date _____

My intention for this week:

_____

_____

_____

Who I can champion this week:

_____

Three Ways I Can Take Care of Myself This Week:

❥ 1. _____

❥ 2. _____

❥ 3. _____

The best three parts of today:

Monday:

1. _____

2. _____

3. _____

Tuesday:

1. _____

2. _____

3. _____

Wednesday:

1. _____

2. _____

3. _____

The best three parts of today:

Thursday:

1. _____

2. _____

3. _____

Friday:

1. _____

2. _____

3. _____

Something I am especially grateful for this week:

_____

_____

_____

Quote of the Week: (funniest thing a student said, a compliment you were given, something inspirational you read)

Three people I can **thank** or **celebrate** this week - in person, in writing, or by making a "day maker" phone call, text or e-mail.

❥ _____ ☐

❥ _____ ☐

❥ _____ ☐

Check as you complete ☑

Random
Doodle
Box

> *"The best and most beautiful things in the world cannot be seen or even touched - they must be felt with the heart."*
>
> Helen Keller

Date _____

My intention for this week:

_____

_____

_____

Who I can champion this week:

_____

Three Ways I Can Take Care of Myself This Week:

❧ 1. _____

❧ 2. _____

❧ 3. _____

The best three parts of today:

Monday:

1. _____

2. _____

3. _____

Tuesday:

1. _____

2. _____

3. _____

Wednesday:

1. _____

2. _____

3. _____

The best three parts of today:

Thursday:

1. _____

2. _____

3. _____

Friday:

1. _____

2. _____

3. _____

Something I am especially grateful for this week:

_____

_____

_____

Quote of the Week: (funniest thing a student said, a compliment you were given, something inspirational you read)

Three people I can **thank** or **celebrate** this week - in person, in writing, or by making a "day maker" phone call, text or e-mail.

❥ _____ ☐

❥ _____ ☐

❥ _____ ☐

Check as you complete

Random
Doodle
Box

> *"Happiness is not something you postpone for the future; it is something you design for the present."*
>
> Jim Rohn

Date _____

My intention for this week:

_____

_____

_____

Who I can champion this week:

_____

Three Ways I Can Take Care of Myself This Week:

❥ 1._____

❥ 2._____

❥ 3._____

The best three parts of today:

Monday:

1. _____

2. _____

3. _____

Tuesday:

1. _____

2. _____

3. _____

Wednesday:

1. _____

2. _____

3. _____

The best three parts of today:

Thursday:

1. _____

2. _____

3. _____

Friday:

1. _____

2. _____

3. _____

Something I am especially grateful for this week:

_____

_____

_____

Quote of the Week: (funniest thing a student said, a compliment you were given, something inspirational you read)

Three people I can **thank** or **celebrate** this week - in person, in writing, or by making a "day maker" phone call, text or e-mail.

➤ _____ ☐

➤ _____ ☐

➤ _____ ☐

Check as you complete ☑

Random
Doodle
Box

> *"Children will not remember you for the material things you provided but for the feeling that you cherished them."*
>
> Richard L. Evans

Date _____

My intention for this week:

_____

_____

_____

Who I can champion this week:

_____

Three Ways I Can Take Care of Myself This Week:

❥ 1. _____

❥ 2. _____

❥ 3. _____

The best three parts of today:

Monday:

    1. _____

    2. _____

    3. _____

Tuesday:

    1. _____

    2. _____

    3. _____

Wednesday:

    1. _____

    2. _____

    3. _____

The best three parts of today:

Thursday:

1. _____

2. _____

3. _____

Friday:

1. _____

2. _____

3. _____

Something I am especially grateful for this week:

_____

_____

_____

Quote of the Week: (funniest thing a student said, a compliment you were given, something inspirational you read)

Three people I can **thank** or **celebrate** this week - in person, in writing, or by making a "day maker" phone call, text or e-mail.

❥ _____ ☐

❥ _____ ☐

❥ _____ ☐

Check as you complete ☑

Random
Doodle
Box

> *"When the sun is shining I can do anything; no mountain is too high, no trouble too difficult to overcome."*
>
> *Wilma Rudolph*

Date _____

My intention for this week:

_____

_____

_____

Who I can champion this week:

_____

Three Ways I Can Take Care of Myself This Week:

- 1. _____

- 2. _____

- 3. _____

The best three parts of today:

Monday:

1. _____

2. _____

3. _____

Tuesday:

1. _____

2. _____

3. _____

Wednesday:

1. _____

2. _____

3. _____

The best three parts of today:

Thursday:

1. _____

2. _____

3. _____

Friday:

1. _____

2. _____

3. _____

Something I am especially grateful for this week:

_____

_____

_____

Quote of the Week: (funniest thing a student said, a compliment you were given, something inspirational you read)

Three people I can **thank** or **celebrate** this week - in person, in writing, or by making a "day maker" phone call, text or e-mail.

❧ _____ ☐

❧ _____ ☐

❧ _____ ☐

Check as you complete

Random
Doodle
Box

> *"Correction does much, but encouragement does more."*
>
> Johann Wolfgang von Goethe

Date _____

My intention for this week:

_____

_____

_____

Who I can champion this week:

_____

Three Ways I Can Take Care of Myself This Week:

❥ 1. _____

❥ 2. _____

❥ 3. _____

The best three parts of today:

Monday:

1. _____

2. _____

3. _____

Tuesday:

1. _____

2. _____

3. _____

Wednesday:

1. _____

2. _____

3. _____

The best three parts of today:

Thursday:

1. _____

2. _____

3. _____

Friday:

1. _____

2. _____

3. _____

Something I am especially grateful for this week:

_____

_____

_____

Quote of the Week: (funniest thing a student said, a compliment you were given, something inspirational you read)

Three people I can **thank** or **celebrate** this week - in person, in writing, or by making a "day maker" phone call, text or e-mail.

❧ _____ ☐

❧ _____ ☐

❧ _____ ☐

Check as you complete ✅

Random
Doodle
Box

> *"The mediocre teacher tells. The good teacher explains. The superior teacher demonstrates. The great teacher inspires."*
>
> William Arthur Ward

Date _____

My intention for this week:

_____

_____

_____

Who I can champion this week:

_____

Three Ways I Can Take Care of Myself This Week:

❥ 1. _____

❥ 2. _____

❥ 3. _____

The best three parts of today:

Monday:

1. _____

2. _____

3. _____

Tuesday:

1. _____

2. _____

3. _____

Wednesday:

1. _____

2. _____

3. _____

The best three parts of today:

Thursday:

1. _____

2. _____

3. _____

Friday:

1. _____

2. _____

3. _____

Something I am especially grateful for this week:

_____

_____

_____

Quote of the Week: (funniest thing a student said, a compliment you were given, something inspirational you read)

Three people I can **thank** or **celebrate** this week - in person, in writing, or by making a "day maker" phone call, text or e-mail.

❥ _____ ☐

❥ _____ ☐

❥ _____ ☐

Check as you complete ✓

Random
Doodle
Box

> *"Our greatest natural resource is the minds of our children."*
>
> Walt Disney

Date _____

My intention for this week:

_____

_____

_____

Who I can champion this week:

_____

Three Ways I Can Take Care of Myself This Week:

❥ 1._____

❥ 2._____

❥ 3._____

The best three parts of today:

Monday:

1. _____

2. _____

3. _____

Tuesday:

1. _____

2. _____

3. _____

Wednesday:

1. _____

2. _____

3. _____

The best three parts of today:

Thursday:

    1. _____

    2. _____

    3. _____

Friday:

    1. _____

    2. _____

    3. _____

Something I am especially grateful for this week:

_____

_____

_____

Quote of the Week: (funniest thing a student said, a compliment you were given, something inspirational you read)

Three people I can **thank** or **celebrate** this week - in person, in writing, or by making a "day maker" phone call, text or e-mail.

- ❯ _____ ☐
- ❯ _____ ☐
- ❯ _____ ☐

Check as you complete

Random
Doodle
Box

> *"Try to be a rainbow in someone's cloud. "*
> Maya Angelou

Date _____

My intention for this week:

_____

_____

_____

Who I can champion this week:

_____

Three Ways I Can Take Care of Myself This Week:

❥ 1._____

❥ 2._____

❥ 3._____

The best three parts of today:

Monday:

    1. _____

    2. _____

    3. _____

Tuesday:

    1. _____

    2. _____

    3. _____

Wednesday:

    1. _____

    2. _____

    3. _____

The best three parts of today:

Thursday:

1. _____

2. _____

3. _____

Friday:

1. _____

2. _____

3. _____

Something I am especially grateful for this week:

_____

_____

_____

Quote of the Week: (funniest thing a student said, a compliment you were given, something inspirational you read)

Three people I can **thank** or **celebrate** this week - in person, in writing, or by making a "day maker" phone call, text or e-mail.

> _____ ☐

> _____ ☐

> _____ ☐

Check as you complete ☑

Random
Doodle
Box

> *"True teachers are those who use themselves as bridges over which they invite their students to cross; then, having facilitated their crossing, joyfully collapse, encouraging them to create their own."*
>
> Nikos Kazantzakis

Date _____

My intention for this week:

_____

_____

_____

Who I can champion this week:

_____

Three Ways I Can Take Care of Myself This Week:

❥ 1. _____

❥ 2. _____

❥ 3. _____

The best three parts of today:

Monday:

1. _____

2. _____

3. _____

Tuesday:

1. _____

2. _____

3. _____

Wednesday:

1. _____

2. _____

3. _____

The best three parts of today:

Thursday:

1. _____

2. _____

3. _____

Friday:

1. _____

2. _____

3. _____

Something I am especially grateful for this week:

_____

_____

_____

Quote of the Week: (funniest thing a student said, a compliment you were given, something inspirational you read)

Three people I can **thank** or **celebrate** this week - in person, in writing, or by making a "day maker" phone call, text or e-mail.

- ❧ _____ ☐
- ❧ _____ ☐
- ❧ _____ ☐

Check as you complete ☑

Random
Doodle
Box

> *"The fruits of your labors may be reaped two generations from now. Trust, even when you don't see the results."*
>
> Henri Nouwen

Date _____

My intention for this week:

_____

_____

_____

Who I can champion this week:

_____

Three Ways I Can Take Care of Myself This Week:

❥ 1._____

❥ 2._____

❥ 3._____

The best three parts of today:

Monday:

1. _____

2. _____

3. _____

Tuesday:

1. _____

2. _____

3. _____

Wednesday:

1. _____

2. _____

3. _____

The best three parts of today:

Thursday:

1. _____

2. _____

3. _____

Friday:

1. _____

2. _____

3. _____

Something I am especially grateful for this week:

_____

_____

_____

Quote of the Week: (funniest thing a student said, a compliment you were given, something inspirational you read)

Three people I can **thank** or **celebrate** this week - in person, in writing, or by making a "day maker" phone call, text or e-mail.

❥ _____ ☐

❥ _____ ☐

❥ _____ ☐

Check as you complete ☑

Random
Doodle
Box

> *"Always do your best. Your best is going to change from moment to moment; it will be different when you are healthy as opposed to sick. Under any circumstance, simply do your best, and you will avoid self-judgment, self-abuse and regret."*
>
> Don Miguel Ruiz

Date _____

My intention for this week:

_____

_____

_____

Who I can champion this week:

_____

Three Ways I Can Take Care of Myself This Week:

➤ 1. _____

➤ 2. _____

➤ 3. _____

The best three parts of today:

Monday:

1. _____

2. _____

3. _____

Tuesday:

1. _____

2. _____

3. _____

Wednesday:

1. _____

2. _____

3. _____

The best three parts of today:

Thursday:

1. _____

2. _____

3. _____

Friday:

1. _____

2. _____

3. _____

Something I am especially grateful for this week:

_____

_____

_____

Quote of the Week: (funniest thing a student said, a compliment you were given, something inspirational you read)

Three people I can **thank** or **celebrate** this week - in person, in writing, or by making a "day maker" phone call, text or e-mail.

❥ _____ ☐

❥ _____ ☐

❥ _____ ☐

Check as you complete ☑

Random
Doodle
Box

> *"There are only two ways to live: you can live as if nothing is a miracle: you can live as if everything is a miracle."*
>
> Albert Einstein

Date _____

My intention for this week:

_____

_____

_____

Who I can champion this week:

_____

Three Ways I Can Take Care of Myself This Week:

> 1. _____

> 2. _____

> 3. _____

The best three parts of today:

Monday:

    1. _____

    2. _____

    3. _____

Tuesday:

    1. _____

    2. _____

    3. _____

Wednesday:

    1. _____

    2. _____

    3. _____

The best three parts of today:

Thursday:

1. _____

2. _____

3. _____

Friday:

1. _____

2. _____

3. _____

Something I am especially grateful for this week:

_____

_____

_____

Quote of the Week: (funniest thing a student said, a compliment you were given, something inspirational you read)

Three people I can **thank** or **celebrate** this week - in person, in writing, or by making a "day maker" phone call, text or e-mail.

❥ _____ ☐

❥ _____ ☐

❥ _____ ☐

Check as you complete ☑

Random
Doodle
Box

"Feeling gratitude and not expressing it is like wrapping a present and not giving it."

William Arthur Ward

Date _____

My intention for this week:

_____

_____

_____

Who I can champion this week:

_____

Three Ways I Can Take Care of Myself This Week:

❥ 1._____

❥ 2._____

❥ 3._____

The best three parts of today:

Monday:

    1. _____

    2. _____

    3. _____

Tuesday:

    1. _____

    2. _____

    3. _____

Wednesday:

    1. _____

    2. _____

    3. _____

The best three parts of today:

Thursday:

1. _____

2. _____

3. _____

Friday:

1. _____

2. _____

3. _____

Something I am especially grateful for this week:

_____

_____

_____

Quote of the Week: (funniest thing a student said, a compliment you were given, something inspirational you read)

Three people I can **thank** or **celebrate** this week - in person, in writing, or by making a "day maker" phone call, text or e-mail.

➤ _____ ☐

➤ _____ ☐

➤ _____ ☐

Check as you complete ☑

Random
Doodle
Box

> *"No act of kindness, no matter how small, is ever wasted."*
>
> Aesop

Date _____

My intention for this week:

_____

_____

_____

Who I can champion this week:

_____

Three Ways I Can Take Care of Myself This Week:

❥ 1. _____

❥ 2. _____

❥ 3. _____

The best three parts of today:

Monday:

    1. _____

    2. _____

    3. _____

Tuesday:

    1. _____

    2. _____

    3. _____

Wednesday:

    1. _____

    2. _____

    3. _____

The best three parts of today:

Thursday:

1. _____

2. _____

3. _____

Friday:

1. _____

2. _____

3. _____

Something I am especially grateful for this week:

_____

_____

_____

Quote of the Week: (funniest thing a student said, a compliment you were given, something inspirational you read)

Three people I can **thank** or **celebrate** this week - in person, in writing, or by making a "day maker" phone call, text or e-mail.

❥ _____ ☐

❥ _____ ☐

❥ _____ ☐

Check as you complete ☑

Random
Doodle
Box

> *"Happiness is the consequence of personal effort. You fight for it, you strive for it, insist upon it ....you have to participate relentlessly in the manifestations of your own blessings."*
> Elizabeth Gilbert

Date _____

My intention for this week:

_____

_____

_____

Who I can champion this week:

_____

Three Ways I Can Take Care of Myself This Week:

❧ 1._____

❧ 2._____

❧ 3._____

The best three parts of today:

Monday:

    1. _____

    2. _____

    3. _____

Tuesday:

    1. _____

    2. _____

    3. _____

Wednesday:

    1. _____

    2. _____

    3. _____

The best three parts of today:

Thursday:

1. _____

2. _____

3. _____

Friday:

1. _____

2. _____

3. _____

Something I am especially grateful for this week:

_____

_____

_____

Quote of the Week: (funniest thing a student said, a compliment you were given, something inspirational you read)

Three people I can **thank** or **celebrate** this week - in person, in writing, or by making a "day maker" phone call, text or e-mail.

❧ _____ ☐

❧ _____ ☐

❧ _____ ☐

Check as you complete ☑

Random
Doodle
Box

"We cannot always do great things. But we can do small things with great love."

Mother Teresa

Date _____

My intention for this week:

_____

_____

_____

Who I can champion this week:

_____

Three Ways I Can Take Care of Myself This Week:

❥ 1._____

❥ 2._____

❥ 3._____

The best three parts of today:

Monday:

1. _____

2. _____

3. _____

Tuesday:

1. _____

2. _____

3. _____

Wednesday:

1. _____

2. _____

3. _____

The best three parts of today:

Thursday:

1. _____

2. _____

3. _____

Friday:

1. _____

2. _____

3. _____

Something I am especially grateful for this week:

_____

_____

_____

Quote of the Week: (funniest thing a student said, a compliment you were given, something inspirational you read)

Three people I can **thank** or **celebrate** this week - in person, in writing, or by making a "day maker" phone call, text or e-mail.

❧ _____ ☐

❧ _____ ☐

❧ _____ ☐

Check as you complete

Random
Doodle
Box

"I've come to a frightening conclusion that I am the decisive element in the classroom. It's my personal approach that creates the climate. It's my daily mood that makes the weather."

Haim G. Ginott

Date _____

My intention for this week:

_____

_____

_____

Who I can champion this week:

_____

Three Ways I Can Take Care of Myself This Week:

❥ 1. _____

❥ 2. _____

❥ 3. _____

The best three parts of today:

Monday:

1. _____

2. _____

3. _____

Tuesday:

1. _____

2. _____

3. _____

Wednesday:

1. _____

2. _____

3. _____

The best three parts of today:

Thursday:

1. _____

2. _____

3. _____

Friday:

1. _____

2. _____

3. _____

Something I am especially grateful for this week:

_____

_____

_____

Quote of the Week: (funniest thing a student said, a compliment you were given, something inspirational you read)

Three people I can **thank** or **celebrate** this week - in person, in writing, or by making a "day maker" phone call, text or e-mail.

❥ _____ ☐

❥ _____ ☐

❥ _____ ☐

Check as you complete ☑

Random
Doodle
Box

> *"Technology is just a tool. In terms of getting the kids working together and motivating them, the teacher is the most important."*
>
> Bill Gates

Date _____

My intention for this week:

_____

_____

_____

Who I can champion this week:

_____

Three Ways I Can Take Care of Myself This Week:

❥ 1._____

❥ 2._____

❥ 3._____

The best three parts of today:

Monday:

    1. _____

    2. _____

    3. _____

Tuesday:

    1. _____

    2. _____

    3. _____

Wednesday:

    1. _____

    2. _____

    3. _____

The best three parts of today:

Thursday:

1. _____

2. _____

3. _____

Friday:

1. _____

2. _____

3. _____

Something I am especially grateful for this week:

_____

_____

_____

Quote of the Week: (funniest thing a student said, a compliment you were given, something inspirational you read)

Three people I can **thank** or **celebrate** this week - in person, in writing, or by making a "day maker" phone call, text or e-mail.

❥ _____ ☐

❥ _____ ☐

❥ _____ ☐

Check as you complete ✓

Random
Doodle
Box

> *"It is the supreme art of the teacher to awaken joy in creative expression and knowledge."*
>
> Albert Einstein

Date _____

My intention for this week:

_____

_____

_____

Who I can champion this week:

_____

Three Ways I Can Take Care of Myself This Week:

❥ 1. _____

❥ 2. _____

❥ 3. _____

The best three parts of today:

Monday:

1. _____

2. _____

3. _____

Tuesday:

1. _____

2. _____

3. _____

Wednesday:

1. _____

2. _____

3. _____

The best three parts of today:

Thursday:

1. _____

2. _____

3. _____

Friday:

1. _____

2. _____

3. _____

Something I am especially grateful for this week:

_____

_____

_____

Quote of the Week: (funniest thing a student said, a compliment you were given, something inspirational you read)

Three people I can **thank** or **celebrate** this week - in person, in writing, or by making a "day maker" phone call, text or e-mail.

❥ _____ ☐

❥ _____ ☐

❥ _____ ☐

Check as you complete ✅

Random
Doodle
Box

> *"I have learned that, although I am a good teacher, I am a much better student, and I was blessed to learn valuable lessons from my students on a daily basis. They taught me the importance of teaching to a student - and not to a test."*
>
> Erin Gruwell

Date _____

My intention for this week:

_____

_____

_____

Who I can champion this week:

_____

Three Ways I Can Take Care of Myself This Week:

❥ 1. _____

❥ 2. _____

❥ 3. _____

The best three parts of today:

Monday:

  1. _____

  2. _____

  3. _____

Tuesday:

  1. _____

  2. _____

  3. _____

Wednesday:

  1. _____

  2. _____

  3. _____

The best three parts of today:

Thursday:

1. _____

2. _____

3. _____

Friday:

1. _____

2. _____

3. _____

Something I am especially grateful for this week:

_____

_____

_____

Quote of the Week: (funniest thing a student said, a compliment you were given, something inspirational you read)

Three people I can **thank** or **celebrate** this week - in person, in writing, or by making a "day maker" phone call, text or e-mail.

❥ _____ ☐

❥ _____ ☐

❥ _____ ☐

Check as you complete ☑

Random
Doodle
Box

> *"The happiness of your life depends upon the quality of your thoughts."*
>
> Marcus Aurelius

Date _____

My intention for this week:

_____

_____

_____

Who I can champion this week:

_____

Three Ways I Can Take Care of Myself This Week:

➤ 1. _____

➤ 2. _____

➤ 3. _____

The best three parts of today:

Monday:

    1. _____

    2. _____

    3. _____

Tuesday:

    1. _____

    2. _____

    3. _____

Wednesday:

    1. _____

    2. _____

    3. _____

The best three parts of today:

Thursday:

1. _____

2. _____

3. _____

Friday:

1. _____

2. _____

3. _____

Something I am especially grateful for this week:

_____

_____

_____

Quote of the Week: (funniest thing a student said, a compliment you were given, something inspirational you read)

Three people I can **thank** or **celebrate** this week - in person, in writing, or by making a "day maker" phone call, text or e-mail.

❥ _____ ☐

❥ _____ ☐

❥ _____ ☐

Check as you complete

Random
Doodle
Box

> *"Each day of our lives we make deposits in the memory banks of our children."*
>
> Charles R. Swindoll

Date _____

My intention for this week:

_____

_____

_____

Who I can champion this week:

_____

Three Ways I Can Take Care of Myself This Week:

❥ 1._____

❥ 2._____

❥ 3._____

The best three parts of today:

Monday:

    1. _____

    2. _____

    3. _____

Tuesday:

    1. _____

    2. _____

    3. _____

Wednesday:

    1. _____

    2. _____

    3. _____

The best three parts of today:

Thursday:

1. _____

2. _____

3. _____

Friday:

1. _____

2. _____

3. _____

Something I am especially grateful for this week:

_____

_____

_____

Quote of the Week: (funniest thing a student said, a compliment you were given, something inspirational you read)

Three people I can **thank** or **celebrate** this week - in person, in writing, or by making a "day maker" phone call, text or e-mail.

❥ _____ ☐

❥ _____ ☐

❥ _____ ☐

Check as you complete

Random
Doodle
Box

> *"I like a teacher who gives you something to take home to think about besides homework."*
>
> Lily Tomlin

Date _____

My intention for this week:

_____

_____

_____

Who I can champion this week:

_____

Three Ways I Can Take Care of Myself This Week:

❧ 1._____

❧ 2._____

❧ 3._____

The best three parts of today:

Monday:

1. _____

2. _____

3. _____

Tuesday:

1. _____

2. _____

3. _____

Wednesday:

1. _____

2. _____

3. _____

The best three parts of today:

Thursday:

1. _____

2. _____

3. _____

Friday:

1. _____

2. _____

3. _____

Something I am especially grateful for this week:

_____

_____

_____

Quote of the Week: (funniest thing a student said, a compliment you were given, something inspirational you read)

Three people I can **thank** or **celebrate** this week - in person, in writing, or by making a "day maker" phone call, text or e-mail.

❥ _____ ☐

❥ _____ ☐

❥ _____ ☐

Check as you complete ☑

Random
Doodle
Box

> *"Be happy for this moment. This moment is your life."*
> Omar Khayyam

Date _____

My intention for this week:

_____

_____

_____

Who I can champion this week:

_____

Three Ways I Can Take Care of Myself This Week:

❥ 1. _____

❥ 2. _____

❥ 3. _____

The best three parts of today:

Monday:

1. _____

2. _____

3. _____

Tuesday:

1. _____

2. _____

3. _____

Wednesday:

1. _____

2. _____

3. _____

The best three parts of today:

Thursday:

1. _____

2. _____

3. _____

Friday:

1. _____

2. _____

3. _____

Something I am especially grateful for this week:

_____

_____

_____

Quote of the Week: (funniest thing a student said, a compliment you were given, something inspirational you read)

Three people I can **thank** or **celebrate** this week - in person, in writing, or by making a "day maker" phone call, text or e-mail.

❥ _____ ☐

❥ _____ ☐

❥ _____ ☐

Check as you complete ☑

Random
Doodle
Box

> *"Teachers who are crazy enough to think they can change the world, usually do."*
>
> Unknown

Date _____

My intention for this week:

_____

_____

_____

Who I can champion this week:

_____

Three Ways I Can Take Care of Myself This Week:

❥ 1. _____

❥ 2. _____

❥ 3. _____

The best three parts of today:

Monday:

    1. _____

    2. _____

    3. _____

Tuesday:

    1. _____

    2. _____

    3. _____

Wednesday:

    1. _____

    2. _____

    3. _____

The best three parts of today:

Thursday:

1. _____

2. _____

3. _____

Friday:

1. _____

2. _____

3. _____

Something I am especially grateful for this week:

_____

_____

_____

Quote of the Week: (funniest thing a student said, a compliment you were given, something inspirational you read)

Three people I can **thank** or **celebrate** this week - in person, in writing, or by making a "day maker" phone call, text or e-mail.

❥ _____ ☐

❥ _____ ☐

❥ _____ ☐

Check as you complete

Random Doodle Box

> *"A teacher takes a hand, opens a mind, touches a heart and shapes the future."*
>
> Unknown

Date _____

My intention for this week:

_____

_____

_____

Who I can champion this week:

_____

Three Ways I Can Take Care of Myself This Week:

❧ 1._____

❧ 2._____

❧ 3._____

The best three parts of today:

Monday:

    1. _____

    2. _____

    3. _____

Tuesday:

    1. _____

    2. _____

    3. _____

Wednesday:

    1. _____

    2. _____

    3. _____

The best three parts of today:

Thursday:

1. _____

2. _____

3. _____

Friday:

1. _____

2. _____

3. _____

Something I am especially grateful for this week:

_____

_____

_____

Quote of the Week: (funniest thing a student said, a compliment you were given, something inspirational you read)

Three people I can **thank** or **celebrate** this week - in person, in writing, or by making a "day maker" phone call, text or e-mail.

❯ _____ ☐

❯ _____ ☐

❯ _____ ☐

Check as you complete ☑

Random
Doodle
Box

> *"Success is not the key to happiness. Happiness is the key to success. If you love what you are doing, you will be successful."*
>
> Albert Schweitzer

Date _____

My intention for this week:

_____

_____

_____

Who I can champion this week:

_____

Three Ways I Can Take Care of Myself This Week:

➤ 1. _____

➤ 2. _____

➤ 3. _____

The best three parts of today:

Monday:

    1. _____

    2. _____

    3. _____

Tuesday:

    1. _____

    2. _____

    3. _____

Wednesday:

    1. _____

    2. _____

    3. _____

The best three parts of today:

Thursday:

1. _____

2. _____

3. _____

Friday:

1. _____

2. _____

3. _____

Something I am especially grateful for this week:

_____

_____

_____

Quote of the Week: (funniest thing a student said, a compliment you were given, something inspirational you read)

Three people I can **thank** or **celebrate** this week - in person, in writing, or by making a "day maker" phone call, text or e-mail.

❥ _____   ☐

❥ _____   ☐

❥ _____   ☐

Check as you complete ☑

Random
Doodle
Box

"That's the real trouble with the world, too many people grow up. They forget. They don't remember what it's like to be twelve years old. They patronize. They treat children as inferiors. I won't do that."

Walt Disney

Date _____

My intention for this week:

_____

_____

_____

Who I can champion this week:

_____

Three Ways I Can Take Care of Myself This Week:

❥ 1. _____

❥ 2. _____

❥ 3. _____

The best three parts of today:

Monday:

    1. _____

    2. _____

    3. _____

Tuesday:

    1. _____

    2. _____

    3. _____

Wednesday:

    1. _____

    2. _____

    3. _____

The best three parts of today:

Thursday:

1. _____

2. _____

3. _____

Friday:

1. _____

2. _____

3. _____

Something I am especially grateful for this week:

_____

_____

_____

Quote of the Week: (funniest thing a student said, a compliment you were given, something inspirational you read)

Three people I can **thank** or **celebrate** this week - in person, in writing, or by making a "day maker" phone call, text or e-mail.

❥ _____ ☐

❥ _____ ☐

❥ _____ ☐

Check as you complete

Random
Doodle
Box

> *"If kids come to us from strong, healthy functioning families, it makes our job easier. If they do not come to us from strong, healthy, functioning families, it makes our job more important."*
>
> Barbara Colorose

Date _____

My intention for this week:

_____

_____

_____

Who I can champion this week:

_____

Three Ways I Can Take Care of Myself This Week:

❧ 1. _____

❧ 2. _____

❧ 3. _____

The best three parts of today:

Monday:

1. _____

2. _____

3. _____

Tuesday:

1. _____

2. _____

3. _____

Wednesday:

1. _____

2. _____

3. _____

The best three parts of today:

Thursday:

1. _____

2. _____

3. _____

Friday:

1. _____

2. _____

3. _____

Something I am especially grateful for this week:

_____

_____

_____

Quote of the Week: (funniest thing a student said, a compliment you were given, something inspirational you read)

Three people I can **thank** or **celebrate** this week - in person, in writing, or by making a "day maker" phone call, text or e-mail.

❥ _____ ☐

❥ _____ ☐

❥ _____ ☐

Check as you complete ☑

Random
Doodle
Box

End of Year Reflections

What are some ways that I grew this year?

_____

_____

_____

What was one pleasant surprise this year?

_____

Who did I grow closer to this year that I hadn't expected?

_____

Who is someone who made my year easier this year that I can thank?

_____

_____

What are some ways I can ensure I regroup and recharge this summer?

_____

_____

_____

What are some resources I can look into during break that will make me more effective next year (books, websites, courses)?

_____

_____

_____

In ten years from now, which students will I still remember who brought me the most joy, made me laugh or caused me to stretch the most?

_____

_____

_____

_____

What else will I remember most about this year?

_____

_____

_____

_____

This Year's All Stars

You can use this space to paste in a photo of this year's class or group of colleagues

"A hundred years from now it will not matter what my bank account was, the sort of house I lived in, or the kind of car I drove... but the world may be different because I was important in the life of a child."

Unknown

Good Karma

I thank you from the bottom of my heart for all that you do for children and education. It is an important and noble endeavor to educate minds and build a solid, bright, hopeful foundation for our collective future. At the heart of it all, are the unsung heroes who show up in classrooms every day. The teachers.

Please Help Spread the Love

- If you enjoyed this journal, please consider gifting a copy to a fellow teacher.
- Also, if you would leave an honest review on Amazon it will help people find this book, and know if it is for them. Every single review is important to me, even if it's just two lines.

You May Also Love

This journal is a companion piece to a book called <u>Positive Mindset Habits For Teachers - 10 Steps to Reduce Stress, Increase Student Engagement and Reingnite Your Passion For Teaching</u>. It's packed with the latest research on positive psychology, exercises and practical advice on how to reduce teacher overwhelm and stress and put passion and joy in your classroom and your life. Find out more at happy-classrooms.com or check it out on Amazon.

Other Versions of This Journal

There are three versions of this journal available. Feedback I received is that it would be fun to have different journal covers for different school years. Also, although the content will be relevant and appeal to all teachers, I am aware that the love heart and floral graphics may not. The academic and blue cover gift editions have more "gender neutral" graphics. Other than the graphics, the content of the journals is the same.

All three versions of the journal are available on Amazon, and at HappyHabitsJournals.com and happy-classrooms.com

Gift Edition
Heart Graphics

Gift Edition
Regular Graphics

Academic Edition
Regular Graphics

About The Author

"Happier classrooms for teachers and students."

Grace is a public school teacher in Northern California. A self confessed "joy junkie", she is the author of the <u>One New Habit</u> book series as well as <u>Positive Mindset Habits for Teachers</u>.

Grace lived and studied in four countries before making California her home. She stepped away from a successful corporate career when she realized that hanging around young, inquiring minds was a really great way to spend her day.

She holds credentials to teach two foreign languages that she has yet to use, and is also a Certified NLP (Neuro-Linguistic Programming) Practitioner. More importantly, she is a mom to two adult children, twenty third-graders, and one too many cats. They all agree she has a contagious love of learning and a very happy classroom.

Made in the USA
Monee, IL
13 December 2020